The Pied Piper of Hamelin

Level 4

Retold by Nicole Taylor

Series Editors: Annie Hughes and Melanie Williams

Pearson Education Limited
Edinburgh Gate, Harlow
Essex CM20 2JE, England
and Associated Companies throughout the world.

ISBN 978-0-582-42872-0

First published by Librairie du Liban Publishers, London 1996
This adaptation first published 2000 under licence by
Penguin Books
2000 © Penguin Books Ltd
Illustrations © 1996 Librairie du Liban

10

Design by Wendi Watson
Illustrated by Angus McBride

Printed in China
SWTC/10

Published by Pearson Education Limited in association with Penguin Books Ltd,
both companies being subsidiaries of Pearson Plc

For a complete list of the titles available in the Penguin Young Readers series
please write to your local Pearson Education office or to:
Penguin Readers Marketing Department, Pearson Education,
Edinburgh Gate, Harlow, Essex, CM20 2JE.

Once upon a time there was a town called Hamelin. Hamelin was in Germany. The streets were long and the houses were old.

There were a lot of people in Hamelin. They loved their town but there was one problem. There were hundreds of rats!

There were rats in the streets. There were rats on the roof tops. There were rats in the church and in the gardens. Everywhere the people looked there were rats.

Now, rats are not bad animals but the rats in Hamelin were big and fat. They had enormous teeth and very long tails. The people of Hamelin were afraid of them.

The rats jumped onto men's hats and into women's baskets. Children were afraid of them and ran away. The rats went into the houses through the windows and under the doors. They even went down the chimneys.

There were hundreds of rats in the houses. There were rats in the bedrooms and rats in the hall. There were rats in the bathroom and the living room. But the room the rats liked best was the kitchen.

They got into the cupboards and onto the shelves. They got into cups and saucepans. They sat on the table and slept in the bowls. Even the cats and dogs were afraid.

The rats were very hungry. They drank the milk and ate the cheese.
They finished all the vegetables and fruit.
They liked bread and cakes and biscuits but their favourite food was chicken.
They ate all the people's food.

They ate the dog and cat food too.
Soon there was nothing left to eat.

The people were very hungry.
They were very unhappy too.

The town had a Mayor. He was an important man. When the people of Hamelin had a problem they went to see the Mayor.

Now, the people were very angry. They did not like the rats and they were very hungry too. There was no more food and no more drink.

They went to see the Mayor.
'We're hungry,' they shouted.
'The rats have eaten all our food.'
'Kill the rats!'
'Please help us.'

The Mayor went to the Town Hall. He spoke to his men. 'The people are very angry,' he said. 'They're hungry because the rats have eaten all their food and they're thirsty because the rats have made all the water very dirty.'

'Yes,' said one man. 'And they are afraid of the rats because they are dirty and they bite.'

What can we do?' asked the Mayor.

The Mayor and his men thought and thought. This kind of thing had never happened in Hamelin before and they did not have any ideas.

'We must kill the rats!' said one man.
'How?' the others said.
'We must frighten the rats away!' said another man.
'How?' the others said.

The Mayor and his men thought and talked for days and days.
Nobody had a good idea.

Then, one day, a strange
man came to the town.

He was tall and thin. His hair
was the colour of gold and
his clothes were part red and
part yellow. He had a big hat
on his head with an
enormous white feather. In his
hand he had a long pipe.
All the men looked at him.
Everyone was quiet.

'I want to speak to the Mayor,' said the man with the pipe.

'I am the Mayor,' said the Mayor.
'Who are you?'

'My name is the Pied Piper.'

'Where are you from?' asked the Mayor.

'I come from a country far away from here,' said the Pied Piper.

What do you want?' asked the men.

'I've heard you have a problem here,'
said the Pied Piper, 'and I think I can
help you. If you pay me well, I'll kill all
the rats for you.'

'How much money do you want?'
asked the Mayor.
'One thousand pieces of gold,'
said the Pied Piper.
'Good, that's a deal,' said the
Mayor. 'I'll pay you one thousand
pieces of gold if you kill all the rats.'

The next day, the Pied Piper took his pipe and went into the street. He began to play a tune. The music sounded very strange.

Some people came out of their houses to listen. Other people looked out of their windows to watch the Pied Piper as he played his pipe.

Then a strange thing happened. When the rats heard the music they came out through the windows and under the doors and began to follow him.

First one rat, then two, then three. Then ten, then twenty. Soon there were hundreds of rats following the Pied Piper as he played his strange music.

When the rats heard the music they came out of the bedrooms and out of the halls. They came out of the bathrooms and the living rooms. They came out of the cupboards and the bowls in the kitchens.

The rats came out of all the houses in Hamelin.

More and more and more of them came out through the windows and under the doors until there was a sea of rats everywhere. Soon there were hundreds and hundreds of rats in the street.

They all followed the Pied Piper.

The Pied Piper played and played until it was very late and quite dark in the street. In the houses, the people of Hamelin lit their candles and looked everywhere for rats. Not one person could find a rat anywhere.
They were all in the street.

' But how will you kill the rats?' asked the people.
'Be patient, you'll see,' said the Pied Piper.

The Pied Piper arrived at the river, but he did not stop. He got into a boat and started to row across the water.

All the people of Hamelin crowded onto the bridge and watched as he continued to play his haunting tune from the middle of the river.

The rats did not stop either. They ran down the steps and into the river and seemed to disappear into the dark water. More and more rats came down the steps and disappeared until there were no rats left in the town.

Suddenly all was quiet.
Then the people of Hamelin watching from the bridge gave a loud cheer.
'Hoorah,' they said. They were very happy.

The people of Hamelin went back to their houses. They opened the doors and windows and cheered.
'Hoorah for the Pied Piper,' they said.
Men and women laughed and talked in the streets.
The cats were not quite so happy, but the dogs ran around barking with excitement.

The Mayor was very happy too.

Then the Pied Piper bowed to the Mayor and said, 'May I have what you promised me now?'

The Mayor began to laugh.
'What did I promise you?' he asked

'Money,' said the Pied Piper,
'You promised me one thousand
pieces of gold, if I killed all
the rats.'

'But you didn't kill the rats
yourself. The water killed the rats.
I won't give you any money!'

The Mayor and his
men laughed.
But the Pied Piper
was very angry.

The Pied Piper did not like the Mayor because he had cheated and hadn't kept his word.

He decided what he would do.
He turned away and walked off down the street, playing his pipe as he went.

The Mayor was very pleased.
There were no more rats in Hamelin and it had cost him nothing to get rid of them.

He laughed and laughed until his nose was red.

The Pied Piper was playing his strange music again, only this time there were no rats to follow him down the street. When the children heard the music, they came out of their houses and into the street just like the rats had done. All the children, big and small, rich and poor, came running out to listen to the music. Even the Mayor's son came out into the street.

The Pied Piper began to run and as he ran he played his music faster and faster. The children ran after him, running through the streets of Hamelin faster and faster as they followed the piper.

'Stop! Stop!' their mothers and fathers shouted. But the children did not listen. They ran on past the houses, down the streets and out of the town.

The Pied Piper ran out of Hamelin and up the mountain. The children ran after him, leaving the town far behind.

There was only one boy who did not run. He had a bad leg and was much slower than the others.

He called to his brothers and sisters, 'Wait for me, wait for me.' But they did not listen. They listened only to the piper's music.

The Pied Piper went up and up towards the mountain. The children laughed, danced and sang as they ran after him. The sound of his music made them feel very happy.

At the top of the mountain there was a huge rock with a big door in the centre. The door opened and a golden light came out. Through the door, on the other side of the mountain, the children caught sight of a magic country.

The Pied Piper went into the mountain through the big door. All of the children followed him in towards the magic country.

Then the big door slowly closed and the children of Hamelin disappeared from sight.

All was quiet and still.

When the little boy with the bad leg arrived at the mountain door, it was closed. He called out to his brothers and sisters but no one replied and he could hear no sound from inside the mountain. He felt very tired and very sad.

He sat down and thought about his brothers and sisters and all the other children. He wanted to cry.

The children's mothers and fathers were very angry.
They went to see the Mayor. 'Where are our children?'
they asked.

'I don't know,' said the Mayor. He was very sorry.

'I didn't give the piper the money I promised him.
Now he has taken our children. I am a stupid man!'

The mothers and fathers went back to look for their children but they only found one boy. The boy with the bad leg told them the story.

The people were very sad.

Nobody ever saw any of the children of Hamelin ever again.

Activities

Before you read the book

Look at the picture and write the words.

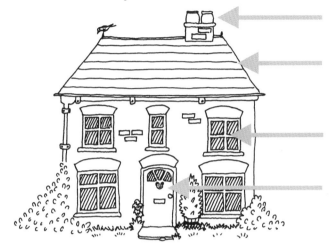

Look at the pictures. Read the words. Draw lines.

wine

fruit

chicken

cheese

bread

vegetables

biscuits

Activities

After you read the book

Look at the pictures and finish the sentences.

There is a rat .... the bowl.

The rats are .... the cart.

The rats are .... the roof.

The rats are .... the street.

Answer the questions.

1. What was the name of the town?

2. What colour were the Pied Piper's clothes?

3. What was the rats' favourite food?

4. How much money did the Pied Piper want?